PRAISE FOR *PADAPILLO*

MW00904321

"A WONDERFUL TOOL FOR PROFESSIONALS WHO WORK WITH FAMILIES — ANY FAMILY FACING SUCH CIRCUMSTANCES WILL FIND THIS STORY INSPIRING AND FULL OF PROMISE."

— Dr. Johnnie Sexton, Au.D., Executive Director / Founder, The CARE Project

---

"FAMILIES WILL LOVE THIS BOOK AND PHYSICIANS, AUDIOLOGISTS, AND EARLY CHILDHOOD PROFESSIONALS WILL BE INSPIRED TO SHARE IT WITH FAMILIES OF CHILDREN WITH HEARING LOSS."

— Deana McGuire Buck, M.Ed., CDC's Act Early Ambassador for Virginia and Affiliate Faculty Member, Virginia Commonwealth University

---

"EVERY FAMILY NEEDS THIS BOOK AT THE TIME OF DIAGNOSIS. THIS BEAUTIFUL STORY OFFERS A GLIMPSE OF A FUTURE THAT IS POSSIBLE AT A TIME WHEN THE JOURNEY AHEAD SEEMS IMPOSSIBLE."

— Ashleigh Greenwood, pediatric audiologist

"THIS BEAUTIFUL STORY REFLECTS THE COMPASSION, LOVE, AND FORTITUDE THAT VALERIE AND HER FAMILY HAVE MODELED IN THEIR OWN EXPERIENCE. THE ENDURING MESSAGE SHE PRESENTS IN THIS BOOK IS THAT WITH LOVE, EDUCATION, AND SUPPORT ALL THINGS ARE POSSIBLE."

— Erin Mahone, Author, Mental Health Advocate and Founder of the If You Could See Me Project

---

"PARENTS OF CHILDREN WITH DISABILITIES OFTEN FEEL MOTIVATED TO PAY IT FORWARD AND TO SHARE THEIR EXPERIENCE WITH THE HOPE IT MAY HELP ANOTHER FAMILY. IN THIS DELIGHTFUL BOOK, VALERIE SHOWS US THE ART AND THE IMPORTANCE OF FINDING OUR VOICE, AND SHARING OUR STORY, AT A TIME WHEN GRIEF AND DOUBT MAY HAVE SILENCED IT."

— Dana Yarbrough, Assistant Director, Partnership for People with Disabilities and Director, Center for Family Involvement, Virginia Commonwealth University

---

"...A BEAUTIFULLY-WRITTEN AND EMOTIONALLY-COMPELLING STORY. THIS BOOK IS BOUND TO BECOME A STANDARD RESOURCE AND WILL SURELY HELP MANY FAMILIES THROUGH THE UNCERTAINTY AND WORRY AFTER RECEIVING A DIAGNOSIS OF HEARING LOSS FOR THEIR CHILD."

— Lori L. Bobsin, Ph.D., CCC-SLP, LSLS Cert. AVT, Coordinator, Aural Habilitation Program at the University of Virginia Cochlear Implant Team

---

"AWARENESS IS ONE OF THE GREAT KEYS TO EMPATHY. WHEN YOU READ THIS BOOK TO CHILDREN, YOU GIVE THEM A DEEPER UNDERSTANDING OF WHAT LIFE IS LIKE FOR THEIR FRIENDS WHO HAVE HEARING LOSS."

— Amy B. McCoy, award-winning author of *Little Big Sister* and *Little Big Sister on the Move*

CENTER FOR
FAMILY INVOLVEMENT

Padapillo

For Justin & family,
Forever grateful, Forever friends.
Valerie James Abbott

WRITTEN BY
Valerie James Abbott

ILLUSTRATED BY
Gina Wojtysiak

Abbott, Valerie. *Padapillo*

Text copyright © 2021 by Valerie James Abbott
Illustrations copyright © 2021 by Gina Wojtysiak
Layout design and logo by Liona Design Co.
Published by KWE Publishing LLC.

ISBN (paperback) 978-1-950306-80-0
ISBN (ebook) 978-1-950306-81-7

Library of Congress Control Number: 2021900368

First Edition. All rights reserved. This book may not be reproduced in whole or in part without written permission from the publisher, except by reviewers who are hereby given the right to quote brief passages in a review. No part of this publication may be reproduced or transmitted in any form or by any means, electronic, mechanical, photocopying, recording, or otherwise without prior permission from the publisher.

KWE Publishing LLC.
www.kwepub.com

Foreword

This little book is a *powerful gift of hope* for families of children with hearing loss. Beautifully illustrated, it reflects on the true story of Bridget's family in seeking information, diagnostic support, and interventions. It also shows us the importance of ongoing developmental monitoring and taking action when concerns are identified.

In addition to being a parent of a child with hearing loss and an experienced family support specialist, Valerie is also a talented and creative writer. She has combined an engaging story with practical information for families, including an index of important resources.

I know that families will love this book and that physicians, audiologists, and early childhood professionals will be inspired to share it with families of children with hearing loss.

Deana McGuire Buck, M.Ed.
CDC Act Early Ambassador — Virginia
Affiliate Faculty Member,
Virginia Commonwealth University

Introduction

In the United States, it is estimated that as many as 3 in 1,000 babies are born deaf or hard of hearing. Late onset or progressive hearing loss can also develop later on during early childhood. Children with undiagnosed or untreated hearing loss often struggle with important developmental milestones. Many of these children are at risk of falling behind in language acquisition, cognitive development, social and emotional well-being, and success in the classroom.

Our daughter, Bridget, passed her newborn hearing screen at the hospital when she was born. At first, she could hear. Then, it changed. We didn't notice. Her hearing loss was not detected until her verbal skills became significantly delayed and we slowly began to admit that something wasn't right. *Padapillo* is based on the true story of how our family discovered and came to terms with the mystery of Bridget's hearing loss, as told through the lens of her older sister, Mary Clare.

In the years that followed her diagnosis, we met many families who had responded to their child's disability just as we had – shocked, worried, and struggling. We each searched for answers, advice, information, and support. This book was written with the intention of being one of many resources, but more importantly it was written as a gift of hope for families who are just beginning their journey.

Because next to love, **hope** is the most powerful fuel of the human spirit.

— Valerie James Abbott

For my greatest treasures — Chris, Mary Clare & Bridie

*May our story encourage others
to never lose sight of hope.*

I thought I knew everything about my little sister, Bridget. After all, she's little. I knew her favorite song. I knew her best friend's name. I even knew how much she hated broccoli.

But there were things I didn't know about her. Like why she did weird things. She never answered the door when the doorbell rang. She didn't notice when a phone would ring. And, she always made me repeat myself. That was annoying. Sometimes she just ignored me. That made me mad. But then there was the strangest thing of all.

One day, Bridget and I were playing on our favorite tree.

"Look!" she said. "A padapillo!"

I looked around, but I didn't see anything.

"What are you talking about?" I asked. "What is a padapillo?"

She pointed to a branch on the tree. I still didn't see the padapillo.

Bridget moved closer. She pointed at a chubby green creature the size of her finger. "Padapillo!" she said again.

I rolled my eyes. "THAT is NOT a PADAPILLO!"

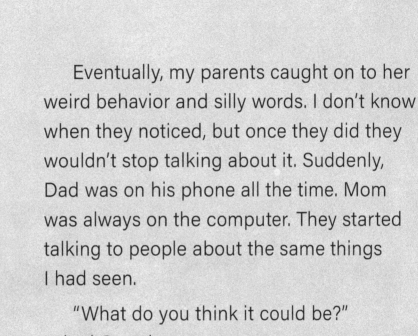

Eventually, my parents caught on to her weird behavior and silly words. I don't know when they noticed, but once they did they wouldn't stop talking about it. Suddenly, Dad was on his phone all the time. Mom was always on the computer. They started talking to people about the same things I had seen.

"What do you think it could be?" asked Grandma.

"We're not sure," said Dad.

One day, my parents took my sister to see a special doctor. It wasn't our regular doctor. It was a new one. No kids in the waiting room, either. Mostly grownups and grandparents.

"Dad," I said.

"Yes, honey?" Dad replied.

"Are these people sick?" I asked.

"No, honey," Dad answered.

"Is Bridget sick?" I asked.

"No, honey. I don't think she's sick," Dad answered.

"Then what are we doing here?" I asked.

Just then, a nurse called us into the doctor's office. Mom held Bridget's hand. She could never follow directions anyway. The doctor asked my parents a lot of questions — too many questions. He looked into my sister's ears.

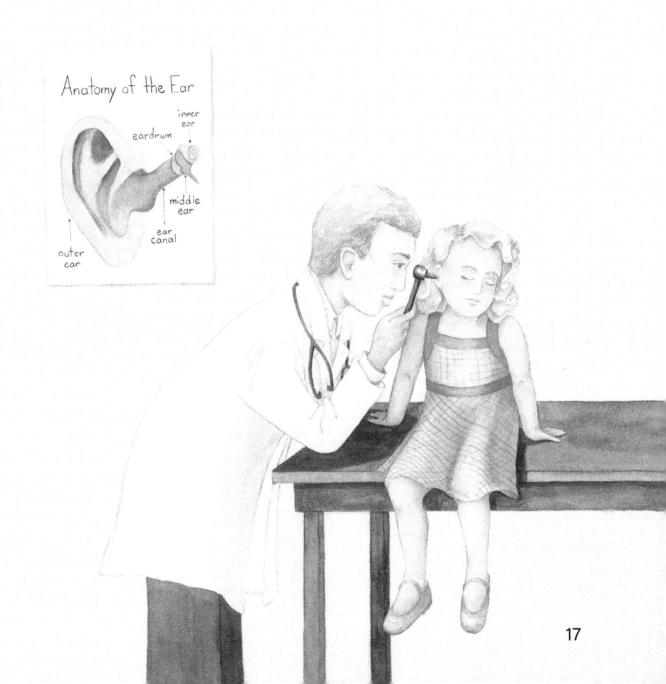

Anatomy of the Ear

inner ear

eardrum

middle ear

ear canal

outer ear

17

18

"You don't have ladybugs in there, do you?"
the doctor joked.

Ladybugs?

"I think I know what might be going on," he said.
"I'd like you to meet Dr. Anna. She is an audiologist."

"What's that?" I asked.

"An audiologist is someone who tests hearing and who
helps people who may not hear well," the doctor told us.

Dr. Anna asked Bridget if she would like to play
a game. This game wasn't like the fun kind we have
at home or at school. It was a listening game.
Bridget wanted to play. It looked
pretty boring to me.

Bridget sat on Mom's lap, in a little metal room with a window and toys inside. I watched as Dr. Anna placed long tubes into Bridget's ears.

"Hey! Are you hurting her?" I asked.

"No, these are soft rubber tubes. They don't hurt. They are like headphones," Dr. Anna explained.

Dr. Anna came out and closed the door to the little metal room. She sat in a chair near the window and waved. She spoke to Bridget through a microphone. "Listen for the beep," she said.

I slumped back in my chair. "This is going to take FOREVER!" I grumbled.

When the game was over, Dr. Anna sat down with me and my parents. "The inside of Bridget's ears don't work like yours and mine. The test shows that she needs something to help make sounds louder and clearer, to help her to hear better. Bridget needs hearing aids."

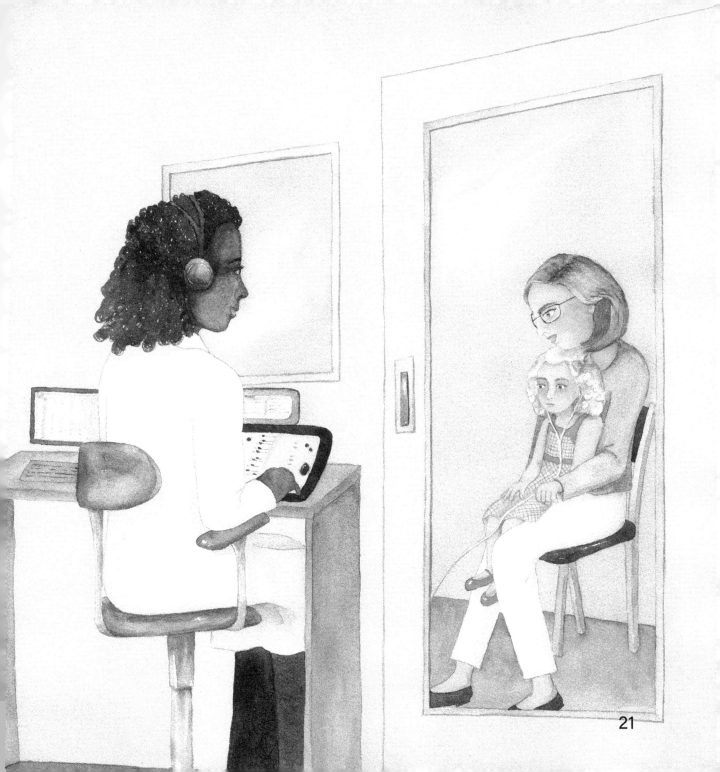

"What!" I shouted. "What are you talking about? She doesn't need hearing aids! My sister can hear just fine!"

Dad wrapped his arm around me. Mom looked sad.

"No, she doesn't hear like you and me," Dr. Anna said. "Bridget can hear some things, but she can't hear other important sounds. I know it might be hard to believe, but it's true."

She then showed us a hearing aid and explained each of the different parts.

Parts of a Hearing Aid

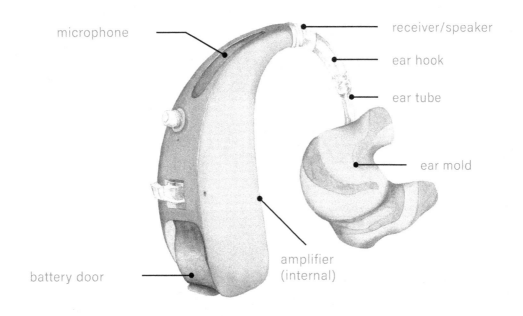

microphone

receiver/speaker

ear hook

ear tube

ear mold

amplifier (internal)

battery door

- The microphone picks up sound.

- Inside, the amplifier makes the sound louder.

- The speaker sends the louder sound into the ear canal through a small tube and an ear mold, which fit inside Bridget's ear.

- The battery provides power to the hearing aid.

24

Next, Dr. Anna squirted blue goo into my sister's ears and said, "This blue stuff will harden into the shape of Bridget's ear canal, so her hearing aid molds will fit perfectly."

Bridget closed her eyes and made a funny face. She said the goo felt squishy.

"What if that gooey stuff gets stuck in there?" I said.

"It won't," Dr. Anna said.

When the blue goo hardened, Dr. Anna gently pulled the molds out of her ears. It looked like the frosting on a cupcake.

"Bridget, did that hurt?" I asked.

She shook her head back and forth. I wondered if she understood what I said.

Dr. Anna kneeled close to my sister and smiled. "Bridget, hearing aids can be any color in the rainbow. Which color would you like?"

Bridget thought about it and pointed to her dress.

"Pink it will be," said Dr. Anna. "I will order them today."

The ride home from the doctor's office took forever. My sister fell asleep. I was so mad. Why hadn't she told me she couldn't hear me? I knew the listening game must be wrong. I knew I had to test her myself as soon as we got home.

"Bridget, come play with me," I said, walking her into my room. "Can you make a block tower? Here, use these."

Bridget ignored me.

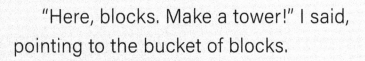

"Here, blocks. Make a tower!" I said, pointing to the bucket of blocks.

"What?" Bridget asked.

"Ugh, let me show you," I said, flipping the bucket upside down. She was so annoying. One block, two blocks, three blocks. Bridget nodded and started her own block tower.

I slowly moved towards my toy chest. I had to find something to prove Dr. Anna and her test were wrong. I had to prove that my sister could hear just fine, and that she was just plain weird.

"Ah ha!" I whispered. I turned around ... I stood behind my sister ... And then ...

RING—ALING—ALING—ALING

Bridget didn't move. She didn't look up. She didn't turn around. She didn't stop at all. She just kept building her block tower.

ALING-ALING-ALING!!!!!

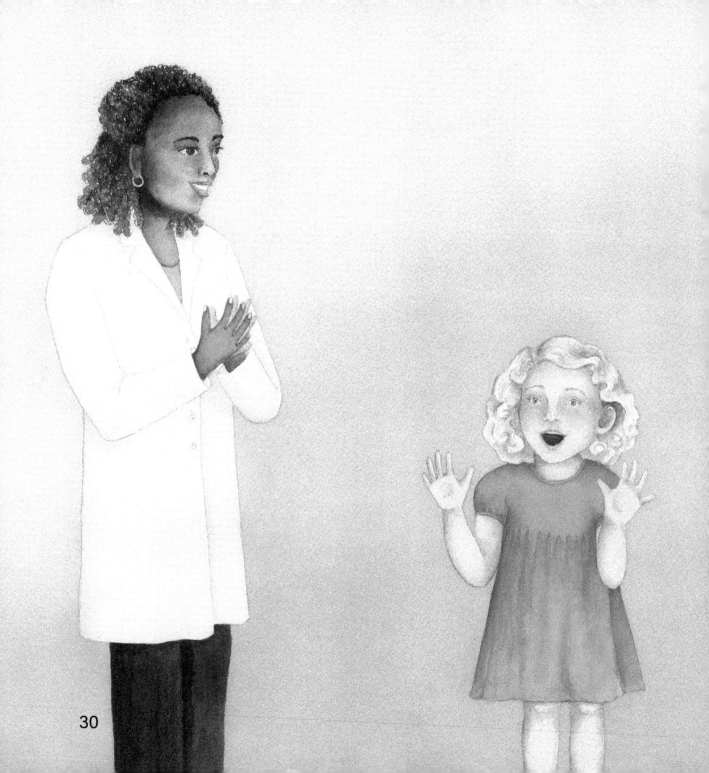

A few weeks later, Bridget's hearing aids were ready. We all went back to see Dr. Anna the audiologist.

Bridget wiggled in the chair. Dr. Anna put the new pink hearing aids in and around her ears. They fit perfectly. "These are so pretty. How do they feel?" Dr. Anna asked.

My sister's eyes grew big and wide. "I hear you!" she said. "I hear you!" We all laughed. Mom cried a little bit. Dr. Anna made some adjustments to the hearing aids. Then, she said we could go home.

Bridget was very excited. She ran down the hall and straight out the door. She wanted to show everyone her new hearing aids.

But then Bridget stopped. She looked around. She grabbed Dad's leg.

"What is THAT?" Bridget asked. She covered her ears.

"What is what?" we asked.

"The noise? Stop the noise!" Bridget began to cry. She grabbed at her ears and started to pull her hearing aids out. I looked around at the moving cars and trucks and people. I didn't hear anything strange. I just heard everyday things.

"It's all right," Mom said. "These sounds are new to you. Don't be afraid." She smiled and picked up my little sister. We headed back to Dr. Anna's office.

"I thought I might see you back here," Dr. Anna said. "Was it loud outside?"

Bridget nodded her head.

"She freaked out," I said.

Bridget wiped tears from her eyes. Dr. Anna made a few more adjustments to the hearing aids. "You are so brave. Keep wearing these every day. It will get easier. I'll see you again very soon."

34

The next day at school, I walked my sister down the hall to her classroom. She squeezed my hand, so I squeezed it back. I felt a tickle in my stomach as we turned the corner. I wondered if anyone would notice her ears. *What would her friends say?*

"Wow! What are those?" Wyatt asked, pointing his finger.

"Hearing aids," Bridget replied. "I can hear better now."

"Let me see! Let me see!" Her friends and teacher gathered around, smiling.

"I love them!" Olivia announced. "They are pink and beautiful!"

My sister let go of my hand and smiled at me. I smiled, too.

Things are a little different now. My sister wears her hearing aids every day. She also works with special helpers called therapists. Sometimes, they ask me to help them!

Bridget doesn't annoy me as much anymore. Actually, she's kind of funny. She won't stop talking and trying new words. She talks to our neighbors when they ring the doorbell. She runs to answer the phone. She still says silly things sometimes and that's okay. But you'll never guess the big new word she said yesterday ...

"Oooh ... butterfly!"

Resources for Families

The following organizations and agencies are dedicated to helping families of children with hearing loss find the information, tools, resources, and support they need:

- Alexander Graham Bell Association for the Deaf and Hard of Hearing: *https://agbell.org/*
- All About Audiology: *https://allaboutaudiology.com/*
- American Society for Deaf Children: *https://deafchildren.org/*
- American Speech Language Hearing Association: *https://asha.org/*
- Centers for Disease Control, National Center on Birth Defects and Developmental Disorders: *https://www.cdc.gov/ncbddd/hearingloss/*
- Early Hearing Detection & Intervention - Pediatric Audiology Links to Services (EHDI-PALS): *https://www.ehdi-pals.org/*

- Family Voices: *https://familyvoices.org/*
- Hands & Voices: *https://handsandvoices.org/*
- Laurent Clerc National Deaf Education Center: *https://www.gallaudet.edu/clerc-center*
- Learn the Signs. Act Early.: *https://www.cdc.gov/ncbddd/actearly/*
- National Center for Hearing Assessment and Management (NCHAM): *https://www.infanthearing.org/*
- National Cued Speech Association: *http://www.cuedspeech.org/*
- National Institute on Deafness and Communication Disorders: *https://www.nidcd.nih.gov/*
- Olive Osmond Hearing Fund: *https://www.hearingfund.org*
- Parent to Parent USA: *https://www.p2pusa.org/*
- The CARE Project: *http://thecareproject.com*

For the most up-to-date list, visit:
https://www.valeriejamesabbott.com/resources

CPSIA information can be obtained
at www.ICGtesting.com
Printed in the USA
JSHW052303210321
12767JS00002B/9

9 781950 306800